James MacMillan

MASS

New English translation 2012
Mixed choir & organ

Boosey & Hawkes Music Publishers Ltd
www.boosey.com

Published by Boosey & Hawkes Music Publishers Ltd
Aldwych House
71–91 Aldwych
London
WC2B 4HN

www.boosey.com

Mass published with the approval of the Department for Christian Life and Worship of the Catholic Bishops' Conference of England and Wales.

ISMN 979-0-060-12590-4
ISBN 978-0-85162-829-5

First published 2013

Printed in England by The Halstan Printing Group, Amersham, Bucks

Music origination by New Notations London
Cover photo by John Daly
Cover design: www.RFportfolio.com

Mass

This Mass was commissioned for the glory of God in the Millennium Year of Jubilee, and was first performed on the Feast of Corpus Christi by the Choir of Westminster Cathedral, London, with Andrew Reid (organ), directed by Martin Baker.

The setting was adapted to the new English translation in 2012. The first performance of this version was given on the Feast of Corpus Christi 2013 by the Choir of Westminster Cathedral, with Peter Stevens (organ), directed by Martin Baker.

First recording (original version): Hyperion CDA67219, by the above performers

Duration: *c*25 minutes

Composer's note: in concert performances of this work the Alleluia, Memorial Acclamation and Great Amen must be omitted.

Note: the original version score remains on sale (ISMN 979-0-060-11299-7)

Contents

Dedicated to Gerry Finn

MASS

for mixed choir & organ

New English translation 2012

JAMES MACMILLAN
(b 1959)

Kyrie

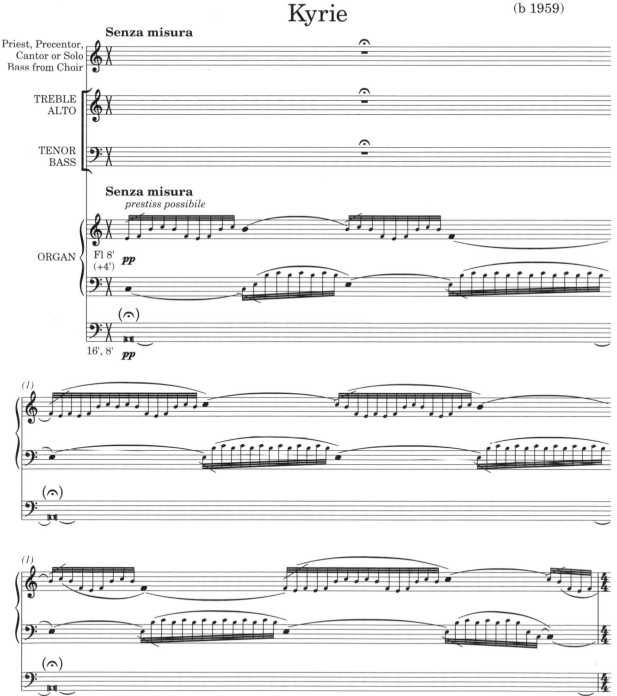

Adagio

Tempo I

(67)

68 PRIEST *mp*

cresc (poco)

You are seat-ed at the right hand of the Fa-ther to in-ter-cede for us: _____
(or: *Lord,* _____ *have* _____ *mer* - *cy,* _____

cresc poco a poco

71

Tr   *ff* Lord, _____ have mer - cy, _____

A   *ff* Lord, _____ have mer - cy, _____

T   *ff* Lord, _____ have mer - cy, _____

B   *ff* Lord, _____ have mer - cy, _____

molto cresc   Full   *ff*

ff

Gloria

Glo - ry to God in the high - - est,____ and on earth____

____ peace _____ to ____ peo - ple of good will.

Soft reed
8' (+4')

16', 8' uncpld

We praise you, we ___ bless you, _____ we a - dore ____

you, _____ we glo - ri - fy _____ you, _____

TENOR

we give you thanks for your great glo - - -

B

we give you thanks for your great glo - - - -

solo:
soft reed
or mutation

8' Str or
Diapason tone

- ry, Lord ___ God, ___ hea - ven - ly King,

- ry, _____ Lord ___ God, ___ hea - ven - ly King, _____

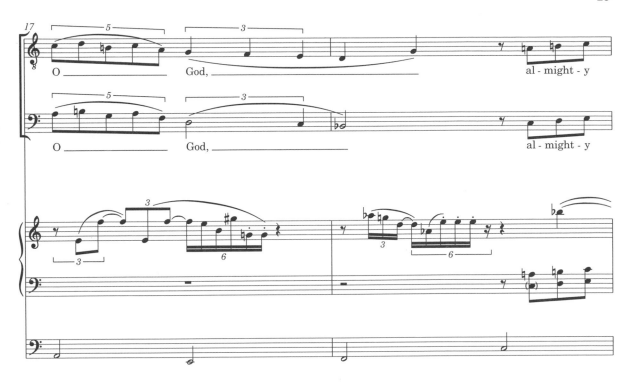

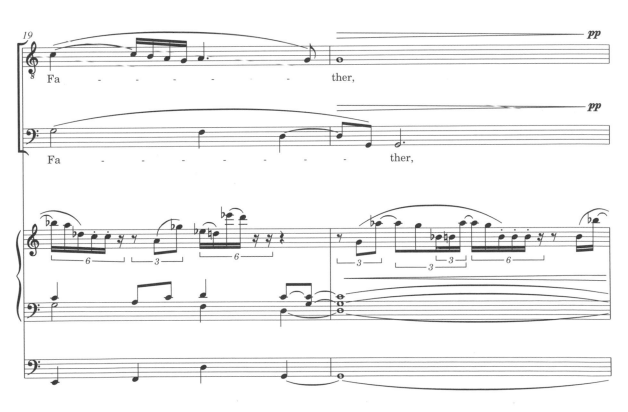

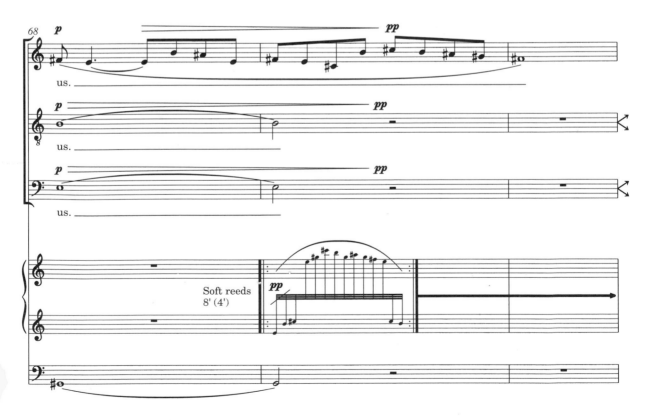

Alleluia

Verse ★

Men only, Trebles only, or solo voice

★ The same cantillation should be used for any Alleluia verse.

Sanctus

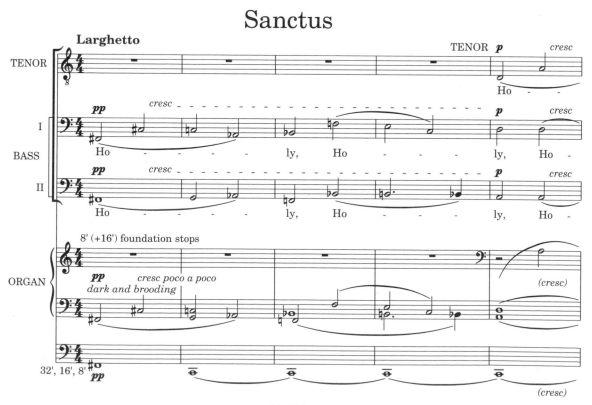

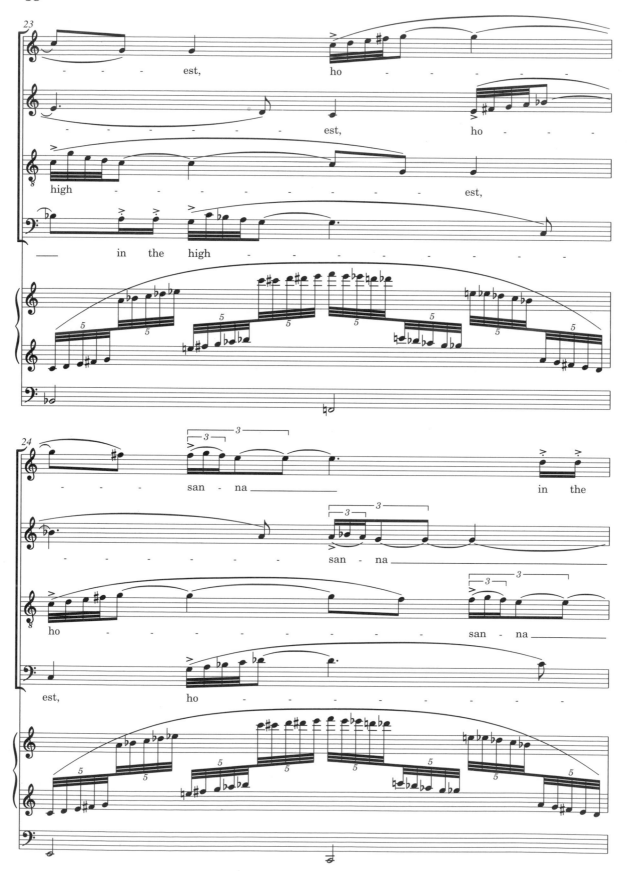

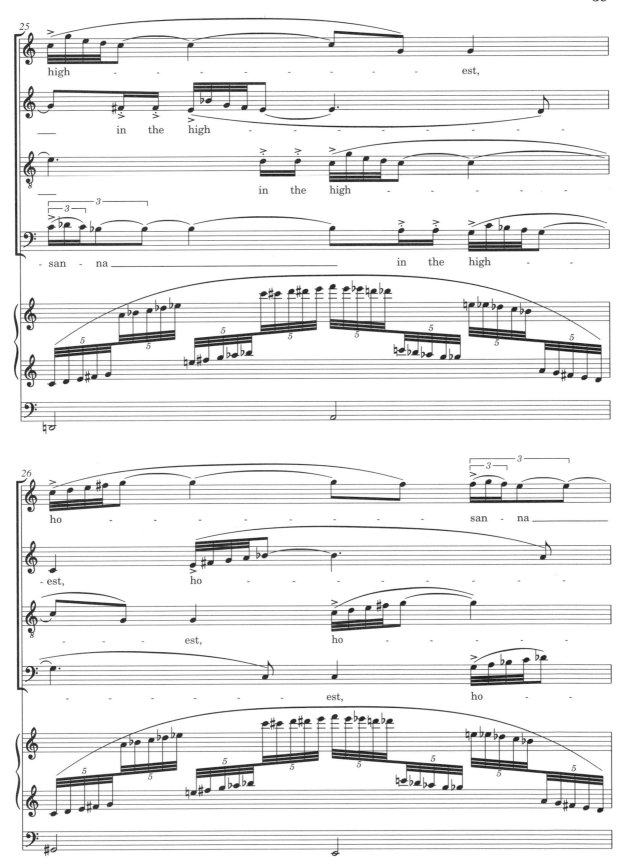

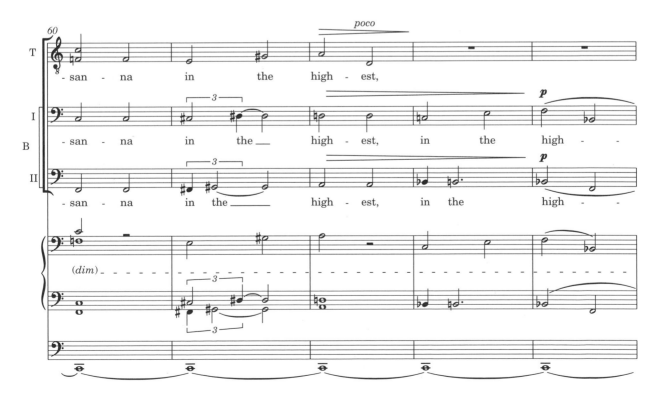

Memorial Acclamation★

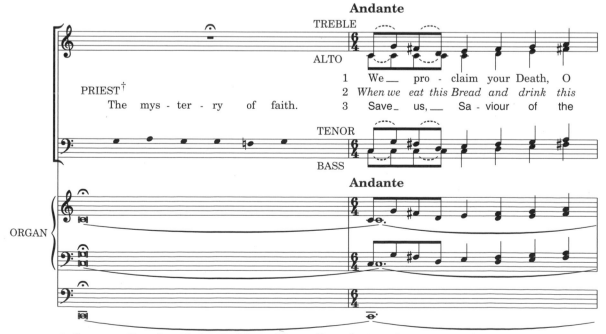

★ Congregation should sing treble and tenor lines, but readers may want
to add alto and bass lines.

† The Missal tone may be used. Starting note: E.

Great Amen⋆

TREBLE
ALTO

A — — men, — a — — —

TENOR
BASS

ORGAN

- men, — a — — — — men. —

⋆ For the Doxology the Missal tone should be used. Starting notes: A–C.
† Congregation should sing treble and tenor lines, but readers may want to add alto and bass lines.

19406

CHOIR ONLY

Agnus Dei

56

19406